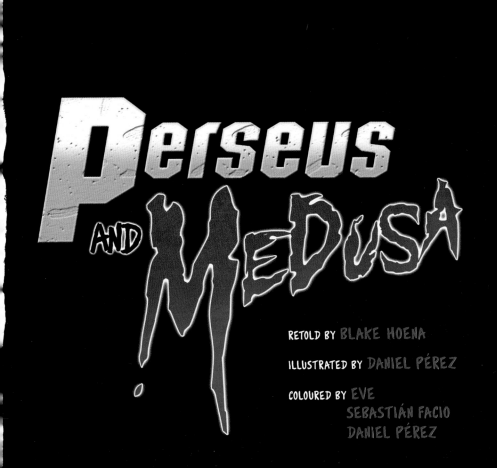

PERSEUS AND MEDUSA

RETOLD BY BLAKE HOENA

ILLUSTRATED BY DANIEL PÉREZ

COLOURED BY EVE
SEBASTIÁN FACIO
DANIEL PÉREZ

www.raintreepublishers.co.uk
Visit our website to find out
more information about
Raintree books.

To order:
☎ Phone +44 (0) 1865 888066
🖷 Fax +44 (0) 1865 314091
🖳 Visit www.raintreepublishers.co.uk

Raintree is an imprint of Capstone Global Library Limited, a company incorporated in England
and Wales having its registered office at 7 Pilgrim Street, London, EC4V 6LB – Registered
company number: 6695582

"Raintree" is a registered trademark of Pearson Education Limited, under licence to Capstone
Global Library Limited

Edited in the UK by Harriet Milles
Originated by Capstone Global Library Ltd
Printed in China by Leo Paper Products Ltd

ISBN 978 1 406 21424 6 (hardback)
14 13 12 11 10
10 9 8 7 6 5 4 3 2 1

ISBN 978 1 406 21429 1 (paperback)
14 13 12 11 10
10 9 8 7 6 5 4 3 2 1

British Library Cataloguing in Publication Data
Hoena, Blake -- Perseus and Medusa
A full catalogue record for this book is available from the British Library.

Contents

Medusa

The Grey Witches

In ancient Argos, Danae and her baby son Perseus were taken down to the sea.

Danae's father, King Acrisius, had been told that she would give birth to a son who would cause the king's death.

Acrisius tried to avoid this fate.

... and the chest was heaved into the sea. Acrisius hoped never to see them again.

But Zeus would not allow his own son to be lost.

He sent powerful winds to guide the chest toward the island of Seriphus.

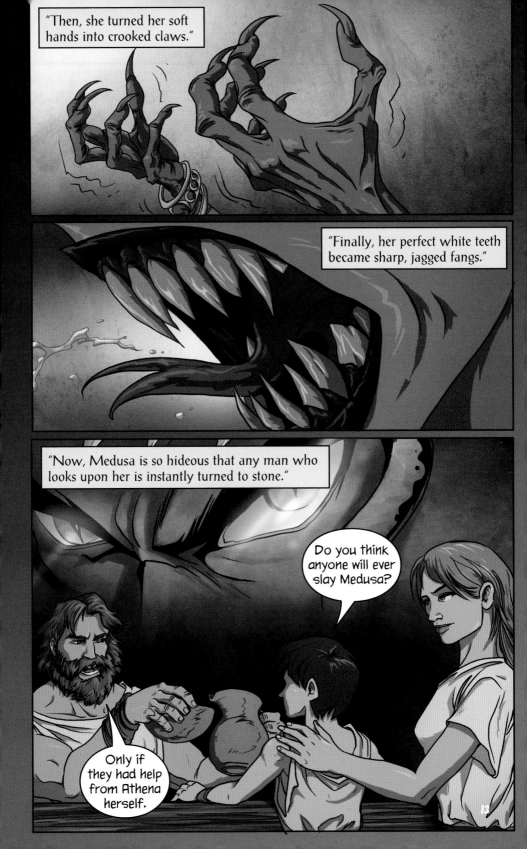

Danae and Perseus lived peacefully until they met King Polydectes.

King Polydectes wished to marry Danae, but she did not love him.

The king did not force Danae to marry him because he feared Perseus, who had grown into a strong, young man.

So, Polydectes searched for a way to get rid of her son.

One day, Polydectes held a great banquet. Guests were expected to bring gifts . . .

Perseus! I see you've come empty handed.

Do you not respect your king?

. . . but Perseus was just a poor fisherman, and could not afford to buy a gift to bring.

It is I who allowed you to make Seriphus your home!

What do you offer me in return?!

I have no items of value to offer, my king.

But if there is something else that you desire, name it —

— and I will get it for you.

Perseus set out immediately to find the Nymphs of the North.

Suddenly, the dense forest gave way to a beautiful gully . . .

Perseus, we three have been waiting for you.

Perseus headed further south past Atlas the giant, towards the ends of the earth.

As Perseus neared his destination, he caught sight of a gloomy swamp.

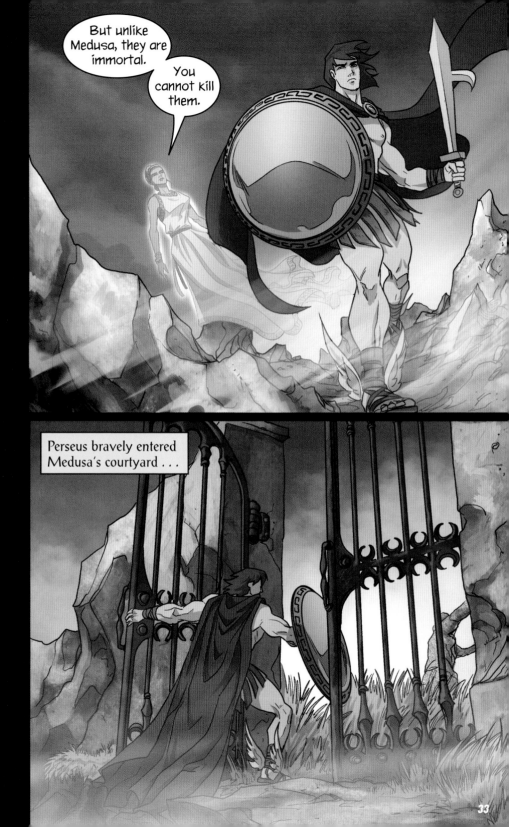

Perseus ventured forth, prepared to face his fate.

HISSSSSSSS

Who dares to enter my domain?

43

AAAAHH!!

After escaping the Gorgons, Perseus flew north, over the African desert.

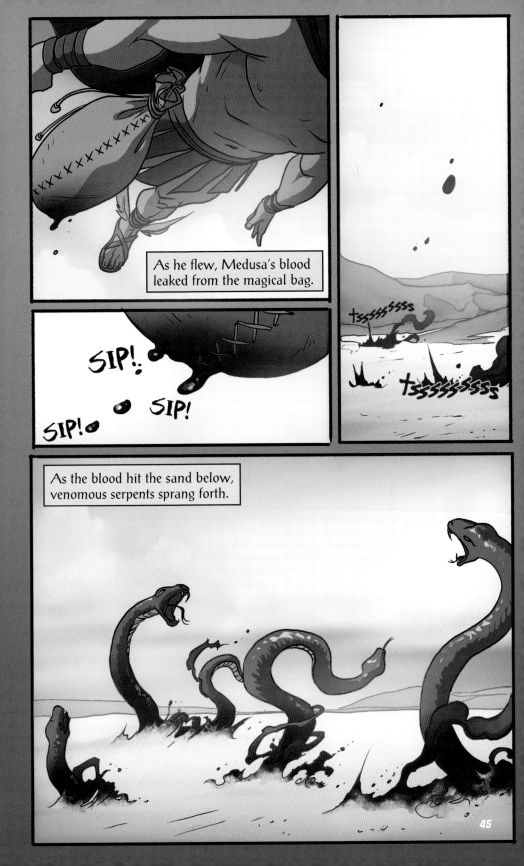

As he flew, Medusa's blood leaked from the magical bag.

SIP! SIP! SIP!

tssssssss

tsssssssss

As the blood hit the sand below, venomous serpents sprang forth.

CHAPTER 5: The Rescue

On his journey home, Perseus passed over Ethiopia, where King Cepheus and Queen Cassiopeia ruled.

As he flew over the coast, something caught his eye.

What's going on down there?

It was Andromeda, daughter of the king and queen.

The sea god Poseidon had sent a sea monster to destroy the kingdom.

The only way to appease Poseidon was for Andromeda to be offered to the sea monster.

Why are you chained to that rock?

My parents said I must be sacrificed to Poseidon.

Otherwise, our kingdom will be destroyed.

But I beg you . . . please save me.

49

KRAKLE!

KRAKLE!

CHAPTER 6: **The Evil King**

After saving Andromeda, Perseus received a message from Dictys.

Polydectes had tried to force Perseus's mother to marry him.

Perseus immediately went to visit the king . . .

Medusa did not kill you as I had hoped.

No, she did not.

Ah, it's Perseus. So the rumours are true.

Then we must fix that problem.

Guards! Kill him!

WOOOOSH!!

After petrifying Polydectes, Perseus made Dictys king of Seriphus as a reward for his friendship and loyalty.

Perseus then gave Medusa's head to Athena, to honour her for helping him on his quest.

Athena mounted the head on her shield, the Aegis, to frighten her enemies in battle.

Perseus returned to Argos with his mother and new wife to make amends with King Acrisius.

But neither Perseus or Danae knew that Perseus was fated to cause Acrisius's death.

The king, having heard rumours of his grandson's return, fled his kingdom.

He travelled to the nearby city of Larissa, in the kingdom of Thessaly.

I've killed my grandfather?!

The prophecy was fulfilled. Danae's son caused the death of King Acrisius.

Despite the accident, Perseus became known as Greece's first great hero.

After his death, Athena placed him in the sky as a constellation, so the whole world would always remember the bravery of Perseus.

How to pronounce Greek names

Name	Pronunciation	Name	Pronunciation
Acrisius	a–KRISS-ee-uss	Ethiopia	eeth-ee-OH-pea-ah
Aegis	AY-jiss	Gorgons	GOR-gons
Andromeda	an-DROM-eh-dah	Hades	HAY-deeze
Argos	AR-goss	Hermes	HER-meeze
Athena	a-THEE-nah	Larissa	la-RISS-ah
Atlas	AT-luss	Medusa	meh-DEW-sah
Bellerophon	bella-RO-phon	Nymphs	NIMFS
Briareus	bry-AIR-ee-uss	Perseus	PER-see-uss
Cassiopeia	cass-ee-oh-PEA-ah	Phineus	FIN-ee-uss
Cepheus	KEF-ee-uss	Polydectes	polly-DECK-teeze
Cerberus	SIR-ber-uss	Poseidon	po-SIGH-dun
Chimera	ky-MAIR-ah	Seriphus	SAIR-i-fuss
Danae	DAN-eye	Thessaly	THESS-ah-lee
Dictys	DIK-teeze	Zeus	ZOOCE
Echidna	eh-KID-nah		

Glossary

appease satisfy or please someone

constellation group of stars with a special shape

desire strong wish or need for something

destiny fate, or something that is guaranteed to happen

domain land or territory owned or guarded by someone

fate things that will happen to someone

gully deep channel worn away by a river or a stream

hideous ugly or horrible

lair place where something or someone eats and sleeps

nymph female spirit or goddess who is closely related to nature

petrify turn to stone

prophecy what a prophet says will happen

prophet person who is able to tell what will happen in the future

quest mission

serpent snake

slay kill in a violent way

Mythical Greek monsters

The ancient Greek myths contain legends of many strange and interesting monsters. Some of them threatened the safety of mankind, while others served important roles in preserving the safety of humans and gods alike.

Briareus was a giant with one hundred arms. He fought with his brothers and with Zeus against the Titans.

Python was a gigantic dragon that terrorized Greece. It was eventually defeated by the powerful arrows of Apollo, god of the sun.

The Chimera was one of the deadliest creatures of Greek myth. The monster was part dragon, part goat, and part lion – and it could breathe fire. It was finally slain by the hero Bellerophon who rode on the flying horse, Pegasus. Bellerophon attacked the monster from the air, avoiding its deadly fiery breath.

Not all of the Greek monsters were enemies of the gods. Cerberus was appointed by the gods to guard the gates of the Underworld, called Hades. He was a monstrous three-headed dog with the lower body of a snake, with even more serpents sprouting from his back. He made sure that only the spirits of the dead entered Hades – the living were not welcome there. More importantly, Cerberus prevented anyone from leaving the world of the dead after they had arrived, ensuring that the spirits of the dead would remain in the Underworld instead of haunting the living.

Each Greek monster had its own unique and special qualities, but most had one thing in common: a mother. Echidna, who lived deep underground, gave birth to almost all of Greek's evil creatures, including Cerberus himself! Echidna's face was beautiful and fair, but she had large wings and a serpent's body. She was so monstrous that she tried to attack the Greek gods themselves! Despite her ferocity, she was utterly beaten. However, the gods allowed Echidna and her children to live so they could test the heroes of Greece.

Discussion questions

1. Perseus was unable to escape his destiny. Do you believe in fate? Why or why not?

2. To find Medusa's lair, Perseus has to trick the sinister Grey Witches. Is it ever all right to trick others?

3. With the help of his winged sandals, Perseus is able to fly. What other superhero qualities does Perseus possess? Do you think he's a superhero? Why?

Writing prompts

1. As Perseus carries Medusa's head over the desert, her blood lands upon the sand, creating venomous serpents. What will happen next? You decide!

2. Athena places Perseus among the stars as a constellation so that his bravery will be remembered by others. What kinds of things would you want others to remember about you? Write about it.

3. Most graphic novels are written and illustrated by different people. Imagine that Perseus has one final task to complete. Write the story of his last task. Then, ask a friend to illustrate your story.

Books in the series

Jason and the Golden Fleece

Brave Jason comes to claim his throne, but the old king will not give up his rule so easily. To prove his worth, Jason must find the greatest treasure in the world, the Golden Fleece.

Theseus and the Minotaur

The evil king of Crete demands that fourteen young Athenians be fed to the Minotaur, a half-man, half-bull. Only Prince Theseus can save them from the fearsome monster that lives deep in the maze-like Labyrinth.

The Adventures of Hercules

The son of a mortal woman and the king of the gods, Hercules is blessed with extraordinary strength. The goddess Hera commands that the mighty Hercules must undergo twelve incredible tasks to pay for a mistake he made in the past.

Perseus and Medusa

Young Perseus grows up, unaware of his royal birth. Before he can claim his heritage, the hero is ordered to slay a hideous monster named Medusa, whose gaze turns men into solid stone. How can the youth fight an enemy he cannot even look at?

Find out more

Websites

http://www.ancientgreece.co.uk/
Visit this British Museum site to find out more about ancient Greek civilization.

http://www.bbc.co.uk/schools/primaryhistory/ancient_greeks/
This site will help you to discover still more about how the ancient Greeks lived and worked. Click on the "Gods and Heroes" link for more fun facts about Greek heroes.

http://greece.mrdonn.org/greekgods/index.html
Find out about the roles and relationships of the ancient Greek gods. The Roman names for some of them are also given on this web page.

Books

Ancient Greece (New Explore History series), Jane Shuter (Heinemann Library, 2007)

Ancient Greece (Time Travel Guides series), Anna Claybourne (Raintree, 2008)

The Ancient Greeks (Understanding People in the Past series), Rosemary Rees (Heinemann Library, 2007)

The History and Activities of Ancient Greece (Hands-on Ancient History series), Greg Owens (Heinemann Library, 2007)

Welcome to the Ancient Olympics!, Jane Bingham (Raintree, 2008)